Olive Ostrich First Radio Show

By Roger Hall

Olive Ostrich

Producer

Mrs. Moneybangles

Mad Jack

Harold Hippo

Shark

Animals

A CLASSROOM PLAY

Scene: *A radio studio. The Olive Ostrich Radio Show is about to go on the air.*

Olive Ostrich: Thirty seconds to the start of my very own radio show. Oh, I'm so excited. I'll be a star.

Producer: Olive! Olive!

Olive Ostrich: Not now, we're almost on the air.

Producer: But Olive!

Olive Ostrich: Hi, this is Olive Ostrich, girl heroine. Olive Ostrich, former assistant to the ace (ho ho, I don't think) detective Harold Hippo. Remember last week, folks,

when I decided to take over from boring old Harold
and his radio show? Tonight, welcome to the first
Olive Ostrich Radio Show! *(She pauses.)*

Producer: What are you waiting for?

Olive Ostrich: The band should have gone da-daaa!

Producer: There is no band.

Olive Ostrich: Well then, sound effects.

Producer: There are no sound effects. I've been trying to
tell you. The tape recorder's been stolen.

Olive Ostrich: What are we going to do? We can't manage without a tape recorder. This week's story depends on sound effects.

Producer: Invite some people from the audience to make the sounds.

Olive Ostrich: OK. Would any of you in the studio audience like to come up and…

(*Various animals come up on the stage.*)

Animals: Moo. Roar. Baaaa. Hiss. Trumpet…

Producer: No noises now, please! You make sounds only when the script indicates it. You'll see as we go along.

Olive Ostrich: Back with you live, folks, on this—the first—Olive Ostrich Radio Show!

Animals: Da-daaa!

Olive Ostrich: Thank you. Olive Ostrich, girl heroine, receives her latest assignment. She is to fly to Africa by jumbo jet…

(*Animals make sound of jet plane. The elephant trumpets.*)

Olive Ostrich: Thank you, Jumbo. Once she had landed, she had to make her way into the heart of this fascinating continent…

(*Animals make sounds of heartbeats.*)

Olive Ostrich: Fearlessly she made her way through the jungle. Then she placed her lovely, long legs into the swamp…

Animals: Squelch, squelch.

Olive Ostrich: Thank you. She came at last to the edge of the jungle. The sky was blue. Up above there were swallows. *(Animals make gulping noises.)*

Olive Ostrich: Suddenly she saw what she was seeking—the camp of Mad Jack McGinty, big-game hunter.

Animals: Panic, panic.

Olive Ostrich: It's only a story. He's not really a big-game hunter; he's an actor.

Mad Jack: In real life, I wouldn't hurt a fly. I'll give you all my autograph afterwards. *(He resumes acting.)* I am the mad hunter. Everything in my sight I shoot. I guide movie stars on safari. I lead royalty to lions and rhinos. This week, my client is Mrs. Moneybangles, who is determined to go home with a big-game trophy.

Animals: Yuk!

Olive Ostrich: Where was I? Oh yes. I creep up to the camp. The excitement is intense. I am so close I can overhear what they are saying.

Mad Jack: Lesson One—firing the gun. Hold the gun to your shoulder.

Mrs. Moneybangles: Like this?

Mad Jack: Not the *barrel* to your shoulder, no. Other way around. Yes. Then you squeeze the trigger...

Mrs. Moneybangles: I'd rather squeeze you, you fascinating man...

Mad Jack *(shocked)*: Please, Mrs. M! This is a family show. Lesson Two—stalking the prey. The wind must be blowing towards us. Otherwise the animals will smell us. One whiff of human and away they run.

Animals: You bet!

Olive Ostrich: Olive followed Mad Jack and Mrs. Moneybangles as they stalked their prey. They saw something. Olive could see Mad Jack lying on the ground.

Mad Jack: Ah! There! I have a tiger in my sights.

Producer: Wrong country!

Mad Jack: Sorr-ree. I see a...a...zebra...

Animals: No. We object.

Mad Jack: Gazelle?

Animals: No.

Mad Jack: Wart-hog?

Animals: No.

Mad Jack: What then? What animal will you let me shoot?

Animals: Shark.

Mad Jack: OK. I see a shark in my sights. Oh, this is stupid. A shark in the heart of Africa!

Olive Ostrich: You must keep going. For the sake of the story. Stay tuned, listeners.

Mrs. Moneybangles: Have you got something for me to shoot yet, cuddles?

Mad Jack *(embarrassed)*: Shush, Marilyn, the listeners will hear. Yes…up in that tree, see.

Mrs. Moneybangles: What is it?

Mad Jack: A rogue shark. Very dangerous this time of year. Have you got him in your sights?

Mrs. Moneybangles: Yes. Now what do I do?

Mad Jack: Fire.

Mrs. Moneybangles: If you say so, gorgeous.

Olive Ostrich: A shot rang out.

Animals: Ring! We mean "bang!"

Shark: Ouch!

(*He falls out of the tree.*)

Animals: Bump.

Mrs. Moneybangles: I shot him, I shot him!

Shark: Listen, this is a lousy part, know what I mean? At least in *Jaws* the shark got to eat people before he got killed. Oh well, let's make the most of it. Give 'em a dying speech. "It is a far, far better thing that I do…"

(*He dies.*)

Animals: Hurrah!

Mrs. Moneybangles: Oh, it's going to look so cute on the living room floor—a shark rug. Oh, Mad Jack, come back with me to my home in Ohio!

Mad Jack: Oh, Marilyn!

Olive Ostrich: With incredible skill I get to within a few feet of the couple. I take photographs.

Animals: Click, click.

Olive Ostrich: And now I'm going to reveal myself to Mad Jack and Mrs. Moneybangles and tell them…

Producer: And so we say farewell to this, the first Olive Ostrich Radio…

Olive Ostrich: Wait, wait! I was supposed to arrest Mad Jack for poaching and smuggling and kissing Mrs. Moneybangles.

Producer: We're out of time, Olive.

Olive Ostrich: I have to show people I am a girl heroine!

Animals: Da-daaaa!

Olive Ostrich: You've ruined my show. Stupid studio audience.

Animals: Boo. Hiss…

(Harold Hippo enters.)

Harold Hippo: Hello there.

Olive Ostrich: Why, it's Harold Hippo. Remember him and his dreary old radio show? Well, Harold, if you're such an ace detective, tell us who stole the tape recorder.

Harold Hippo: I did.

Olive Ostrich: Scream, shout, rage, pound fists on ground, if I had any fists.

Harold Hippo: Yes, folks, stay tuned next week for the return of The Harold Hippo Radio Show!